*With love to my godchild Sarah
and her brother Ian*

Some of the toys
in this book can be found
in the British Museum in London and
in the museum in Salisbury, Wiltshire. I am grateful to
family and friends for lending me their toys: my husband Evan,
my sons James and Julian, and Hilary, Mike, Catherine, Jenny, Anna, Emily, Yvonne,
Christopher, Dinah, Daniel, Deborah, the twins Dana and Michelle, Sarah and Ian, Bar,
Sandy, Katie, Sophie, Louise, Susan G., Ian B., Ant, Marlene, David, Philip, Linda's James,
Joyce and Julie, Dena, Terry, Simone, Valerie, Judy, Mary, Cathy, and to my mother
whose monkey Jacko is now nearly 100 years old. I would also like to thank Susan
Dickinson for her help with the text. The last word must be for my husband Evan whose
support and professional guidance have been invaluable to me while working on this book.

First published in Great Britain by HarperCollins Publishers Ltd in 1993. This mini abridged
edition published 1995. Text and illustrations copyright © 1993 Lesley Anne Ivory
Edited by Susan Dickinson. Cover design by Ian Butterworth
A CIP catalogue record for this title is available from the British Library.
The author asserts the moral right to be identified as the author and illustrator of the work.
ISBN: 0 00 198113-7

Produced by HarperCollins Hong Kong. This book is set in 14/17 Bembo

LESLEY ANNE IVORY

CATS AMONG THE TOYS

Collins
An Imprint of HarperCollinsPublishers

It is not only the people who receive presents in our house. The cats have presents too. They enjoy toy mice and toys that roll along or move. Octopussy's favourite is a tiger, but he is always mislaying it, and he can be seen looking for it all through this book.

Children's toys have amused kittens from the time when cats and people started sharing homes. The Egyptian, Roman and Victorian toys on this page can be found in museums, and the Victorian marbles and jacks belong to friends. Octopussy is sitting on the Noah's Ark I bought for my son Julian.

While Octopussy is busy trying to find his tiger, let me show you the collection of toys belonging to family and friends. I was five when my father gave me the little family of rabbits who live in the felt shoe. The tiny grey teddy was one of my first birthday presents as was Lion Cub whose button can be found in the button border on another page.

Tread carefully over our hall floor. There may be the odd marble left from the kittens' game. It is an ideal surface for games. When the front door is open each marble sheds a pool of coloured light on the tiles.

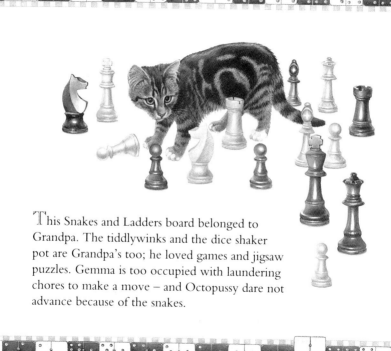

This Snakes and Ladders board belonged to Grandpa. The tiddlywinks and the dice shaker pot are Grandpa's too; he loved games and jigsaw puzzles. Gemma is too occupied with laundering chores to make a move – and Octopussy dare not advance because of the snakes.

Muppet is colour coding, stripe against stripe, beside my collection of wooden cats, of which the tallest one was made by James. I bought the rocking cat in the market one Saturday morning. A friend of Granny's brought the little horse back from India, years ago, and I loved it so much that she gave it to me.

I found this wonderful horse and jockey at a local antique fair. Its workings have practically worn out, but there is a key at the back that makes its legs work a little bit. The little black dog belonged to my husband Evan. When wound up, it wags its tail and shakes the sock. The cuckoo flute is made from silver birch wood and blows "cuckoo". This was part of my Red Indian kit. The policeman on his horse was given to James for his first birthday and it is James's cat Sheena who is playing with the little train.

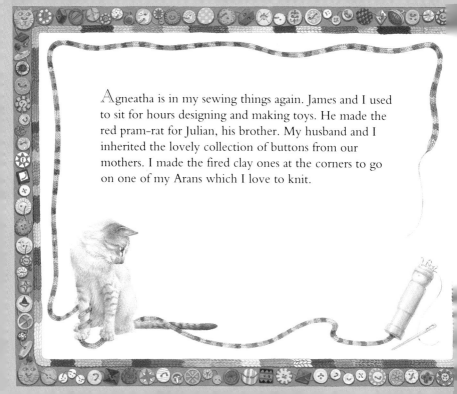

Agneatha is in my sewing things again. James and I used to sit for hours designing and making toys. He made the red pram-rat for Julian, his brother. My husband and I inherited the lovely collection of buttons from our mothers. I made the fired clay ones at the corners to go on one of my Arans which I love to knit.

Ah, there is Octopussy still looking for his tiger, rummaging amongst the dolls' undies. Some of these dolls are quite old. The china doll, Dorothy, belonged to my mother. She sits on the window seat nowadays. Malteazer and her mother Gabby offer Dorothy silent companionship.

Evan and my godchild Sarah built this castle specially for me. The kittens soon altered the design I'm afraid. My old bear Ted Exlington can be seen flopped over the rocking horse. I knitted the clown for Julian's first birthday. He loved it flat and I had to restuff it several times.

Here I have reconstructed my own dolls' house from a tiny black and white photograph, which my father took when I was four. Old Bob, the grey dog on wheels, was one of my favourites. I used to ride him around everywhere. My doll Bluebell is seen here with a Fairy Tale book that belonged to Mother. All the dolls in the border are existing ones from family and friends. Surely Octopussy can't miss his tiger this time!

Ah, Octopussy has found his tiger at last. The bricks give clues to its whereabouts throughout these pages. If you turn over and look carefully among the medley of toys you will see where Octopussy finally put his tiger for safety. Oh, no, Motley has seen where...